Creativity
Workbook

Creativity
Workbook

100 Exercises to Stimulate Creative Thinking

BRENDAN EMMETT QUIGLEY

FALL RIVER PRESS

New York

FALL RIVER PRESS

New York

An Imprint of Sterling Publishing
387 Park Avenue South
New York, NY 10016

© 2011 by Quirk Packaging, Inc.

Design by woolypear

ISBN: 978-1-4351-3268-9

Printed and bound in China

10 9 8 7 6 5 4 3 2 1

Contents

Introduction

Creativity is often considered a gift—a mysterious well of inspiration from which the lucky few who have it draw brilliant new ideas. The truth is, however, that everyone has the ability to be creative. **CREATIVE THINKING IS A SKILL** that can be learned, honed, and nurtured.

People often confuse creativity with artistic expression. Though that is certainly one way in which creativity manifests, **TRUE CREATIVITY ENCOMPASSES MORE** than that—it is the ability to approach and resolve problems in unexpected ways, whether these are practical, emotional, artistic, or spiritual.

The main qualities necessary for creative thinking are focus and open-mindedness. Focus means **THINKING DEEPLY** about something—really looking at the details, following a train of thought farther than you might usually take it, giving yourself time to truly concentrate. Open-mindedness requires you to approach the world with curiosity, give yourself **PERMISSION TO PLAY** (and make mistakes), and offer serious consideration to unconventional or illogical notions.

This book is filled with exercises designed to help you **BREAK OUT** of familiar thinking patterns and embrace new ideas. All you need to begin is a pencil and a willingness to experiment. None of these activities requires special skills; they are **SIMPLE AND FUN** for anyone to do. Also included are some exercises specifically designed for more than one person, so you can tap into a group's collective creativity—try these with family members, friends, or even colleagues.

When you are describing,
A shape, or sound, or tint;
Don't state the matter plainly,
But put it in a hint;
And learn to look at all things,
With a sort of mental squint.

LEWIS CARROLL

As you approach these simple exercises, allow yourself to be open, playful, and imaginative. **THERE ARE NO WRONG ANSWERS!** Try a new activity each day, and you will soon find your creative self expanding in unexpected and wonderful ways, sparking innovation, insight, and fresh ideas in all areas of your life.

Million-Dollar Question

An eccentric billionaire gives you $1,000,000, no questions asked. What would you do with it?

What if the billionaire tasked you with spending none of it directly on yourself?

What if the billionaire will give you an additional $1,000,000 if you spent the first million only outside your home country? Now, how would you spend the money?

The Straight Ink

There's an interesting deal at the Linear Tattoo Parlor: for one day only, tattoos made up entirely of straight lines are 50 percent off. What does your tattoo look like?

All in the Details

In order to be creative, you need to take the time to notice the world around you. It's often the details that make an experience memorable or meaningful. Answer these questions to gauge your capacity for attention to detail.

What time did you go to bed last night?

What side of your mouth do you usually brush first?

What was the last song you heard?

What did you eat for lunch 2 days ago?

Which shoe did you put on first this morning?

What is the mileage displayed on your car's odometer?

What page are you on in the book you're reading?

How many trees are outside your bedroom window?

Who was the last person to call you?

What was the last gift you gave?

How much money are you carrying right now?

When did you last cry?

What color underpants are you wearing?

To whom was the last person you said, "I love you"?

What was the last thing you paid cash for?

What day of the week was your birthday this past year?

Conflicting Advice

We often hear that "many hands make light work," but it's also true that "too many cooks spoil the broth." You should always "look before you leap," yet, "he who hesitates is lost." And every banker will tell you, "a penny saved is a penny earned," while we all know "you can't take it with you."

How many other pairs of aphorisms can you think of that offer conflicting advice?

A hunch is creativity trying to tell you something.

FRANK CAPRA

Personal Day

An announcement has just been made that there will be a national holiday in your honor.

Describe in detail how your holiday will be celebrated.

> *And by the way, everything in life is writable about if you have the outgoing guts to do it, and the imagination to improvise. The worst enemy to creativity is self-doubt.*
>
> **SYLVIA PLATH**

From A to Z

As any artist will tell you, freedom is key to creative pursuits. But sometimes, constraints can actually force us to be more creative. Can you tell a story using only twenty-six sentences? Did I mention that you have to start each sentence with the next consecutive letter of the alphabet? Eventually you'll get back to the letter you started with (you don't have to start with A, by the way). For this exercise, try to plan your story ahead. Give yourself plenty of time to set up the more challenging letters like Q, X, and Z. If you haven't noticed by now, I've been doing this myself in this very write-up. Just look at the first letters of each sentence for proof!

It is better to create than to be learned, creating is the true essence of life.
BARTHOLD GEORG NIEBUHR

> *It is in the compelling zest of high adventure and of victory, and in creative action, that man finds his supreme joys.*

ANTOINE DE SAINT-EXUPERY

Can You Digit?

Imagine a world where we all have six fingers on each hand. Draw a picture of a hand with the new finger in position.

What should the sixth finger be called? What will it be used for?

Silent Movie

Go to a video website on the Internet and press play on a random video. Now, watch the video without any sound. Think about voices and dialogue for the video. If there are no people, could you narrate the story? Below, write the dialogue for the video or the narration.

> *The thing that makes a creative person is to be creative and that is all there is to it.*
>
> **EDWARD ALBEE**

You're the CEO

Find a board game that has letter tiles and randomly select seven letters. Now, using all of these tiles, scramble the letters to form the name of a fictional-yet-realistic-sounding company. Don't worry if it's gibberish; there's a good chance that you'll have to make up a word with these random letters. Besides, there are many current companies, like Google, with made-up names.

As the president of your newly coined company, describe what services your company makes or provides. Does the way your company's name is spelled or pronounced affect your business decisions?

Pitch Perfect

A good pitch for a movie should be only two sentences long. For instance, here's the pitch for *Groundhog Day*: "A cranky, rude man has to relive the worst day of his life over and over again until he gets it right. When he does, he finds true love." Write the pitches for two of your favorite movies.

Now, find a way to combine the two pitches into one pitch for a brand-new movie.

Abstract Emotions

Choose a piece of abstract art, that is, a painting, photograph, or sculpture that represents its subject in a non-realistic way. Look at the piece for several minutes. Now write down how it makes you feel, and what you think the artist might have been feeling while creating it.

> *Every act of creation is first of all an act of destruction.*
>
> **PABLO PICASSO**

No Right

Due to an edict passed by your local government, right turns are declared illegal.

Think of the layout of your neighborhood, specifically the points of interest that you visit often (e.g., your best friend's house, the grocery store, your child's school, etc.). Map the most direct routes to your common destinations so that you make no right turns while traveling.

Right on the Money

There's been an announcement that a World Currency will be debuted with these notes for circulation: 5, 10, 25, 50, 100, 200, and 500.

Consider which historical figures should be featured on the front of the new notes and why. Remember: Think globally.

> *Creativity is merely a plus name for regular activity... any activity becomes creative when the doer cares about doing it right, or better.*
>
> **JOHN UPDIKE**

List Serve

Quick! Write down the first twenty words that pop into your head. Write the entire word, even if halfway through you change your mind. Don't correct your misspellings, either.

1. _____   11. _____

2. _____   12. _____

3. _____   13. _____

4. _____   14. _____

5. _____   15. _____

6. _____   16. _____

7. _____   17. _____

8. _____   18. _____

9. _____   19. _____

10. _____   20. _____

Now, analyze your train of thought through this word exercise.

_____

_____

_____

_____

_____

_____

Don't Look Now…

Looking into a mirror, draw a self-portrait without looking down at the paper while you're drawing.

Brain

Your mind might feel like it's going a mile a minute, but science has proven otherwise. You usually have only seven or eight unique thoughts in your brain at any given moment.

With this in mind (pun intended!), make a pie chart of your brain, showing all of your conscious thoughts at this particular moment. Your foremost or strongest thoughts should take up more room than your fleeting thoughts.

MY BRAIN

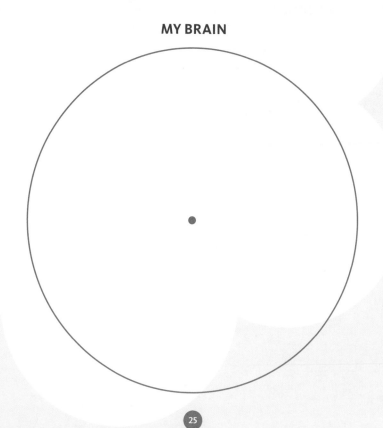

Pack It In

Packing for a trip has become so difficult lately, what with all the restrictions placed on flying. Dizzy Airlines' rates are affordable, but there are even more restrictions applied. First, think of a destination you'd like to visit. For example purposes, I've chosen to go to Peru. Now, paying attention to the restrictions for each of the following travel packages, try to come up with as many items as you can to bring to your destination.

TRAVEL PACKAGE #1: While packing for this trip, your list must only include things that begin with the last letter of the thing you most recently packed, starting with the last letter of your destination. Since I'm going to Peru, the first thing I pack must begin with a U, say, an umbrella. The next item must begin with an A, so I'll bring an anorak. To continue: khakis, sunscreen, novel...

TRAVEL PACKAGE #2: Due to space constraints, you are only allowed to carry on things that have the same number of letters as your destination. Since Peru has four letters, I'm only allowed to bring four-letter objects, like cash, an iPod, soap, and a visa.

TRAVEL PACKAGE #3: Customs has become very strict in defining contraband. For this package, no items containing any of the letters used in spelling the destination will be allowed. That it is to say, for my vacation to Peru, no items may contain the letters P, E, R, or U. So far I've brought a knapsack, socks, sandals, a flashlight, and a comb.

All Hands on Deck

A playing card company has designed a handful of new games that require 104 cards, specifically, eight suits of 13 cards each. They plan on keeping the clubs, spades, diamonds, and hearts.

Design one card in each of the four new card suits.

Eight Is Enough

It is often said that there are only seven basic stories in Hollywood: overcoming the monster, rags to riches, the quest, a voyage and return, tragedy, comedy, and rebirth.

Come up with an eighth basic storyline.

Imagination is the beginning of creation. You imagine what you desire, you will what you imagine, and at last you create what you will.

GEORGE BERNARD SHAW

First Things First

What was your earliest memory? Perhaps it was a sound, smell, or color?

If it's a visual impression, try to draw it. Otherwise, describe it in words.

Stop Signs

Time has come for a complete revamp of the street signs currently used. You've been tapped to contribute to the project.

Design the new "STOP" sign.

Odd Number

It's been an exciting day in mathematics, as a brand new whole number has been discovered between 7 and 8.

You have been called upon not only to name the number, but also to design its character.

Getting Personal

Though they've moved from the back pages of magazines and newspapers to the virtual pages of the Internet, personal ads remain a popular way to seek out companionship. Compose some personal ads for the characters listed below.

1. Your pet

2. Your dentist

3. A mouse living in your home

4. Your boss

5. A vampire

> *The secret to creativity is knowing how to hide your sources.*
>
> **ALBERT EINSTEIN**

Shadow Play

Set up an object or a group of objects as a still life. However, instead of drawing the objects, draw only their shadows. You might want to adjust the lighting so that the shadows being cast are dramatic.

Musical Musings

Quick! Open the nearest magazine or book to a random page and place your finger on a word or phrase.

Now, imagine that this word or phrase is the name of a musician and that you are that performer. Choose your instrument and your sound. What is your look? What are some of your song titles and album names?

> *The writer who possesses the creative gift owns something of which he is not always master—something that at times strangely wills and works for itself.*
>
> **CHARLOTTE BRONTË**

Finish the Doodle #1

The person who started this drawing has become distracted by something else.

Can you complete the picture for him?

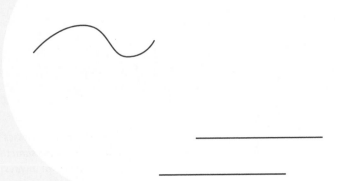

Pitch Perfect

The key to good advertising is to convince people they cannot live without the thing that is being sold. Advertisers are required to be truthful, but sometimes they stretch their claims.

Choose a mundane, everyday object and try to truthfully portray it using outrageous advertising claims. Come up with a new name for this object, as well as marketable selling points. For instance, a binder clip might be a "Portable Document Holder! With an attractive hardback case!" While duct tape might be an "All-in-one Fix-it Wondertool. Capable of repairing everything from old sneakers to leaky faucets!"

> *Creativity requires the courage to let go of certainties.*
> **ERICH FROMM**

Vice Squad

Suddenly, the number of deadly sins has jumped from seven to ten. What are the new vices that go along with wrath, greed, sloth, pride, lust, envy, and gluttony? Describe each new vice.

1.

2.

3.

Clothes-Minded

Everyone has his or her own sense of style. If you were a member of the opposite sex, describe or draw how you would adjust your current style of dress to suit your new gender.

Come Together

Write a song about your family or friends. Dedicate each verse to one person or couple, then create a chorus that ties everyone together.

Time in a Capsule

Put together a list of ten things to include in a time capsule. The items have to be representative of your life. What will you include and why?

1.

2.

3.

4.

5.

6.

7.

8.

True creativity often starts where language ends.

ARTHUR KOESTLER

9.

10.

My Inner Child Could Draw That

Channel your five-year-old self by drawing a scene using crayons only.

Two Sides to Every Story

Think of an event from your life. Now describe this event so that every other sentence is 100 percent true, while the alternating sentence is a total lie.

> *The creative urge is the demon that will not accept anything second rate.*
>
> **AGNES DE MILLE**

> *In this country we encourage "creativity" among the mediocre, but real bursting creativity appalls us. We put it down as undisciplined, as somehow "too much."*
>
> **PAULINE KAEL**

Do the Reshuffle

Take an old magazine and cut any random page into fourths. Reshuffle the pieces and place them together so that the pictures and/or words recombine to something strange and new. List these items here. What do the new words mean? What should you call the new images? By the way, parts of the book *Naked Lunch* by William Burroughs were written this way.

I can't understand why people are frightened of new ideas. I'm frightened of the old ones.

JOHN CAGE

Coming Soon

Imagine that a random photograph, one you might have taken or a published one in a magazine, is the basis for a movie poster.

What is the title of this movie? Come up with the tagline, as well as the general theme and/or plot of the film.

> *For a creative writer, possession of the "truth" is less important than emotional sincerity.*
>
> **GEORGE ORWELL**

Studio Time

Design the layout and furnishings of a rectangular, one-room studio apartment. Do not add walls! Everything must be in the same room.

Now, try the same exercise with an L- or a T-shaped room.

Short Take

Write a short yarn with words that have just one vowel sound.
Translation: Write a short story using words that have only one syllable each.

What's the Answer?

Could you write a scene with dialogue between two people that consists only of questions? Why would they be answering each other's questions with questions? Could answers be implied? Did you know that entire scenes of Tom Stoppard's play *Rosencrantz and Guildenstern are Dead* were series of questions? Do you want to give it a try? Do you think you could go ten sentences?

> *You can't use up creativity. The more you use, the more you have.*
>
> **MAYA ANGELOU**

Emote It

Emotions have become part of modern language. See if you can draw a picture of the following emotions without using any references to the human form, specifically people and faces.

HAPPINESS

SADNESS

ANGER

EXCITEMENT

FEAR

Never Say Never

Are there any things you would never, ever do? Why not?

And despite saying "never," is there any way you could be convinced to do one of these forbidden things?

Singing Fool

Take a favorite song of yours and make up a parody of the lyrics to the chorus. You might want to listen to Weird Al Yankovic's "Eat It" for inspiration...

> *Creativity is allowing yourself to make mistakes. Art is knowing which ones to keep.*
>
> **SCOTT ADAMS**

Your Left Foot

Draw a self-portrait. However, frame the picture so as to not include your head. Instead, focus on a distinctive feature, like a tattoo or a childhood scar, or a body part, like your hand or foot.

Emblematic

Design a coat of arms. Yes, your family's name may already have one, but for the purpose of this exercise, design a new one specifically for your nuclear family. Incorporate colors and symbols that are meaningful.

Draw a Conclusion

Place a picture—any picture will do—along the side of this page. "Finish" the picture by continuing the lines and/or subject matter. For example, if the picture has your family standing in front of your house, and only the half of the porch is seen, continue drawing the porch. If you have chosen an unfamiliar picture, complete it using your imagination.

Put It in Perspective

Assemble a still-life composition out of readily available objects.

Now, imagine that you are an ant on the floor. Draw the still life from your new perspective.

Stop Watch

Imagine you had the ability to stop and start time on your own whim.

Describe ways you could use this power for good and for evil.

> If you are unhappy with anything . . . whatever is bringing you down, get rid of it. Because you'll find that when you're free, your true creativity, your true self comes out.

TINA TURNER

The Nose Knows

Imagine a moment of minor crisis—nothing earth-shattering. It could be something as mundane as the confusion you might have while looking for misplaced keys.

Imagine while in this situation that as a reflex, one of your senses becomes heightened to the point of nearly rendering the other senses useless. Now, imagine that this sense is smell. How would you go about handling your problem with this enhancement?

Whether you believe you can, or whether you believe you can't, you're absolutely right.

HENRY FORD

Finish the Doodle #2

The person who started this drawing has become distracted by something else.

Can you complete the picture for her?

Dream On

Design your dream car. Sure, it can be a real car, but it can also be a strictly fanciful vehicle. Consider how many people it seats, as well as its shape, color, accessories, cargo space, engine capacity, and gas mileage.

Come up with a novelty license plate for your dream machine.

Upside Down
You're Turning Me

Place a simple line drawing in front of a mirror. Now, try to copy the picture by just looking at its reflection. (Your sketch should be upside down compared to the original drawing.)

For an added challenge, try the same exercise using your non-dominant hand.

Finish the Doodle #3

The person who started this drawing has become distracted by something else.

Can you complete the picture for him?

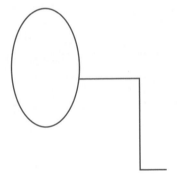

Music Speaks

Select a short (five to ten minutes) piece of music—something without words—with which you are not familiar. It can be any style of music, but it should be something you have never, or rarely, heard before. Listen to it several times.

Now write a story based on the impression and emotions that the music evokes in you.

But, if you have nothing at all to create, then perhaps you create yourself.

CARL JUNG

Mixed It Up

An anagram is a scrambling of letters into other words. Some examples of apt anagrams include THEY SEE for THE EYES, and DIRTY ROOM for DORMITORY.

List the names of 10 friends or places, and try to scramble the letters to come up with anagrams that describe them.

1.

2.

3.

4.

5.

6.

7.

8.

9.

10.

Two-Wheeler

Think about a team sport that you feel you know well, such as football, soccer or baseball. How might that game change if the athletes played while riding bicycles? In what ways would the game be harder or easier? Make your notes below, and try to sketch a likely play.

Cockney Tea Time

Cockney rhyming originated in the epnoymous district of London's East End. It consists of expressions formed from phrases that rhyme with a word, then substituted for the original word. For instance, you take the "apples and pears" instead of "stairs," you'd spend "bees and honey" instead of money, and you use your "north and south" instead of your mouth.

Use the space below to create your own Cockney rhymes. Start with words you use frequently, then try some less common ones.

Making the simple complicated is commonplace; making the complicated simple, awesomely simple, that's creativity.

CHARLES MINGUS

Stage Direction

Hit television shows often search for new ways to be creative, and a favorite is the musical episode. Famous examples include *Buffy the Vampire Slayer*'s "Once More, with Feeling" and *Scrubs'* "My Musical."

Think about turning your favorite show, book, or even a typical day at work into a musical. Would you change the setting or era? What are the main plot points? Who are your characters? Make a list of the songs these characters would sing.

> *Creativity comes from trust. Trust your instincts. And never hope more than you work.*
>
> **RITA MAE BROWN**

In a Word

Pick 10 meaningful people in your life—they can be family members, friends, or co-workers—and compose a one-word description for each person.

1.

2.

3.

4.

5.

6.

7.

8.

9.

10.

Pets Rock

In 1975, the novelty item known as the Pet Rock became enormously popular. What non-living item would you choose as a pet and why?

> Don't think. Thinking is the enemy of creativity. It's self-conscious, and anything self-conscious is lousy. You can't try to do things. You simply must do things.
>
> **RAY BRADBURY**

Holi-dazed

August needs a new major holiday. Come up with a plausible holiday for one or more of its thirty-one days. How will it be celebrated?

One very important aspect of motivation is the willingness to stop and to look at things that no one else has bothered to look at. This simple process of focusing on things that are normally taken for granted is a powerful source of creativity...

EDWARD DE BONO

Power Trip

The superpower question is always a fun one to contemplate!
Would you rather...

...be invisible or fly? Why?

...have superhuman strength or superhuman diplomacy? Why?

...be the smartest person or the fastest? Why?

...have the ability to read minds or the ability to change minds? Why?

...be able to see through walls or hold your breath for hours? Why?

...be able to communicate with animals or have the ability to
shape-shift into any animal? Why?

...be able to predict the future or manipulate the past? Why?

Time's on Your Side

Imagine a day that is completely free. Money is no object, and you don't have to attend to any of your normal daily obligations.

Now, schedule this wide-open day in as explicit detail as you can.

6:00 AM		3:00 PM	
6:30 AM		3:30 PM	
7:00 AM		4:00 PM	
7:30 AM		4:30 PM	
8:00 AM		5:00 PM	
8:30 AM		5:30 PM	
9:00 AM		6:00 PM	
9:30 AM		6:30 PM	
10:00 AM		7:00 PM	
10:30 AM		7:30 PM	
11:00 AM		8:00 PM	
11:30 AM		8:30 PM	
12:00 PM		9:00 PM	
12:30 PM		9:30 PM	
1:00 PM		10:00 PM	
1:30 PM		10:30 PM	
2:00 PM		11:00 PM	
2:30 PM		11:30 PM	

Get Negative

For this exercise, it's all right to think negatively...about space, that is.

Pick a simple object to draw. Instead of outlining the shape of the object, then shading inside the lines, shade around the white (positive) space to form the shape of your object.

That's a Rap

A freestyle rap is an improvised lyric composed in the moment. When multiple rappers are singing together, the song emerges from their combined creatvity, with one rapper's words inspiring the next. Try an improvised group rap—here's how to do it:

The first rapper drops one line. From there, all participants drop two lines each. The first line should rhyme with the previous line, and the second line will be the basis for the next rapper to rhyme. Designate one member of the group to record the lyrics below.

It is good taste, and good taste alone, that possesses the power to sterilize and is always the first handicap to any creative functioning.

SALVADOR DALI

The New Breed

"New" dog breeds, such as the cockapoo or the labradoodle, which are more properly known as "crossbreeds," are very popular. What would happen if you could cross humans with animals and create a new creature? Think of a good human/animal cross. Draw your new creature below, and describe the qualities you think it would possess.

Musical Chairs

In 1950, the composer Leroy Anderson wrote a short orchestral piece called "The Typewriter," whose main instrument was, you guessed it, a typewriter. The musician playing the typewriter would type in sync with the rest of the orchestra. In live concerts, John Fishman of the jam band Phish would routinely do an extended solo coaxing odd noises from a vacuum cleaner. At times, he would blow through the tube as if it were a saxophone. Explore how the everyday objects below can be used to make "music." Consider the ways the objects are designed to be used—what sounds could be made? And then think up some unexpected ways these items could be used to make musical noise.

TOASTER

DOOR KNOB

COFFEE MAKER

LAMP

DOORMAT

Get in Shape

Draw a portrait (of yourself or someone else) using only triangles, circles, squares, and rectangles.

Sleep on It

For one week, keep this book next to your bed. When you wake up each morning, immediately record your dream(s). Make a note of any ways in which your dreams incorporate things you are thinking about, seeing, and dealing with in your daily life. Do any themes recur?

NIGHT #1

NIGHT #2

NIGHT #3

> *Creativity involves
> breaking out of
> established patterns
> in order to look at things
> in a different way.*
>
> **EDWARD DE BONO**

NIGHT #4

NIGHT #5

*The opposite of
creativity is cynicism.*

ESA SAARINEN

NIGHT #6

> *There is the happiness which comes from creative effort. The joy of dreaming, creating, building, whether in painting a picture, writing an epic, singing a song, composing a symphony, devising new invention, creating vast industry.*
>
> **HENRY MILLER**

NIGHT #7

SOS!

Contemplate a common scenario in which you might need to
ask a stranger for help. Unfortunately, you can neither speak nor
pantomime your needs. Instead, you'll have to draw pictures to
effectively communicate your point. Use the space below to draw
your call for help. When you're done, show the pictures to someone
else. Does this person understand what you need?

Colorful Feelings

Color evokes emotion very effectively. For example, anger is often associated with the color red, tranquility with the color blue, and cheerfulness with the color yellow. Assign colors to the emotions and states of mind listed below.

PRIDE

REGRET

DISCOVERY

AMUSEMENT

WORRY

LOVE AT FIRST SIGHT

PARANOIA

GRATITUDE

Now Hear This

This will be an all-day exercise. Each time you hear a sound today, write down the noise it makes and what you think it is. Note how the sound makes you feel. At the end of the day, review your list. Are there any surprises?

NOISE	SOURCE OF SOUND	REACTION

Finish the Doodle #4

The person who started this drawing has become distracted by something else.

Can you complete the picture for her?

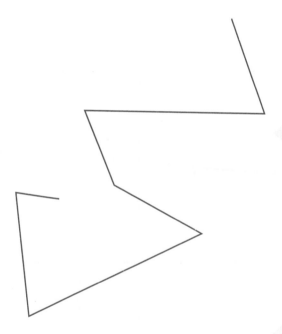

Comic Effect

Comics tell a story in panels. Pick a simple series of actions—examples could be making breakfast, unpacking a suitcase, or planting a seed—and draw it in the panels below. You may use a thought or speech bubble in one panel only. Give your comic a title.

TITLE

Lyrical Journey

Write a story in which every sentence consists of a line from a favorite song.

Family Album

You decide to form a family music group. Design the cover of your debut recording.

An Apple a Day...

Imagine that for one day the only food you can eat is . . .apples.
Make a list of the dishes you would prepare for breakfast, lunch,
and dinner. You may have access to a spice rack.

BREAKFAST

LUNCH

DINNER

Logo-a-gogo

A logo is designed to be instantly recognizable and to visually convey the qualities the entity it represents wants people to associate with it. Some great examples include the Nike Swoosh and the Olympic rings. Design a logo that represents you or your family. Try to make it simple, memorable, and representative of who you are. When you're done, test it by showing your logo to a few friends and see if they can guess what it represents.

Letter Rip

In the classic game of Acronyms, you take the first letters of a word or name and use them to come up with adjectives to describe the word or name. For instance, "Erin" might become Energetic, Rambunctious, Intelligent, and Nearsighted.

Play Acronyms using your first name.

> *Above all, we are coming to understand that the arts incarnate the creativity of a free people. When the creative impulse cannot flourish, when it cannot freely select its methods and objects, when it is deprived of spontaneity, then society severs.*
>
> **JOHN F. KENNEDY**

Now, use the letters of your name to spell out a sentence that applies to you. For example, if Erin was a very good writer, you might say, "Editing rarely is needed."

_____

_____

_____

_____

_____

_____

As an added challenge, play Acronyms with words that end with the letters of your name. In the case of Erin, she might be Suave, Popular, Chichi, and Driven.

_____

_____

_____

_____

_____

_____

_____

Ultimate Dinner Party

You may invite twelve people—it doesn't matter if they're alive or dead—to attend a dinner party. Make a list below of who will be joining you, and note why have you chosen each person.

1.

2.

3.

4.

5.

6.

7.

8.

9.

10.

11.

12.

Assuming money is no object, and the world's finest chefs are at your beck and call, put together the menu for your dinner party, from starters through dessert. Don't forget the drinks and wine list!

APPETIZERS   **BEVERAGE(S)**

MAIN COURSES   **BEVERAGE(S)**

DESSERT   **BEVERAGE(S)**

Turn, Turn, Turn

Start a sketch of something. Anything. It really doesn't matter what the subject is. What does matter is that you stop drawing after five seconds. Then rotate this book 90 degrees to the right or to the left. Playing off this new alignment, create a new drawing using your original sketch.

Blast to the Past

You have a one-way time machine in which you can travel back to any point in your life and live again from that point forward.

What moment would you return to and why? Would you do anything in the past to radically alter your life now?

> *Creativity is piercing the mundane to find the marvelous.*
>
> **BILL MOYERS**

Be Snappy

Write a slogan that snappily describes each of the following things in your life:

HOMETOWN

NEIGHBORHOOD

GROUP OF FRIENDS

JOB

WORK COLLEAGUES

PET

BEST VACATION

FAVORITE SPORTS TEAM

FAVORITE FOOD

Colorama

This exercise requires a visit to a hardware or design store to collect a variety of paint chips in different colorways. Cut them up so that the names are removed. Then select 5 colors that you like or find interesting. Now make up an evocative name for each color that is at least two words but not more than three words long.

1.

2.

3.

4.

5.

Finish the Doodle #5

The person who started this drawing has become distracted by something else.

Can you complete the picture for her?

Opening and Closing Lines

This is a fun exercise for two people. Imagine the opening line of a book you'd like to read. Now write it down on the first line, below. Without sharing what you've written, ask your partner to imagine the last line of a book he or she would like to read, and to write that on the last line on this page. Now look at the lines together, and imagine the plot points necessary to get from the opening line to the closing line, and write them on the lines in between.

Climate Out-of-Your-Control

You're packing for a beach vacation. Your destination has an average temperature of 85°F (29°C) with a zero percent chance of rain. You'll be staying in a secluded hut with a private beachfront. Choose ten things to bring along on your trip. Why have you chosen each item?

1.

2.

3.

4.

5.

6.

7.

8.

9.

10.

There's just one little problem. While traveling, your plane hits a rough patch and crash-lands on a remote, snowy mountain. Thankfully, you and your suitcase survive the crash just fine, but the plane has disintegrated. How might the items you packed be used to help you survive in the climate opposite of what you expected?

Tool Trip

Nothing is handier than a compact, all-in-one pocket tool. Design your ideal pocket tool, but there's a catch: You're stranded on a deserted island with only this tool at your disposal. And it can have only five attachments.

What will those five attachments be and why?

1.

2.

3.

4.

5.

Decorator's Dilemma

You've just bought your dream house. It has been built in the shape that is currently the rage—the octagon. Draw your new home's floor plan. How can you make best use of the space?

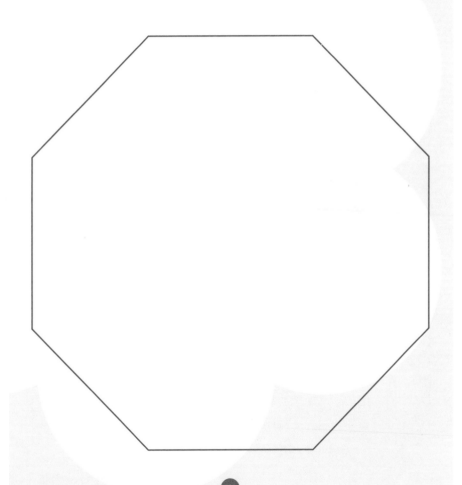

Search Me!

Construct a random word search in which words may be found going up, down, and diagonally. Overlap the words as many times as possible so that every square is used in at least one word.

Construct another word search, but this time all of the words have to be connected by a theme. Overlap the words as many times as possible so that every square is used in at least one word.

Solve the Crime

Walk into a nearby room in your home. It doesn't matter which room it is, or if it's impeccably organized or an utter disaster area.

Now, imagine that you are a private investigator, and this is the scene of a crime. It is up to you to deduce, by visual clues, what crime took place here—it might be especially tricky if things look to be in order and undisturbed.

Use the space provided to sketch the crime scene. What "evidence" has been left behind? Are there any telltale clues that lead to a suspect? Do not infer things that aren't immediately obvious. Use only the information that you can see. Note how you think the crime went down.

> *You must have a room, or a certain hour or so a day, where you don't know what was in the newspapers that morning... This is the place of creative incubation... If you have a sacred place and use it, something eventually will happen.*

JOSEPH CAMPBELL

You've Got
to Represent

You've been asked to design a mascot that will represent your country at a very important world sporting event. How can you represent the most distinctive elements of your country in the mascot's outfit and appearance? Use the space below to sketch your ideas for the mascot.

It's Got Personality

Anthropomorphization is the act of attributing human qualities or motives to things that are not human. Look around the room, and pick out 5 objects. Now ascribe a personality to each one. Your refrigerator, for example, might be cold and unfriendly. On the other hand, perhaps it is generous and inviting. Once you've given each item a human quality, think about how that reflects on you—does it reveal anything about your current mood, desires, or concerns?

1.

2.

3.

4.

5.

Make a Mandala

In the Hindu and Buddhist spiritual traditions, a mandala is a sacred represenation of the universe, often taking the form of a circle with a colorful, repeating, symbolic pattern radiating from the center. Drawing and coloring mandalas is considered to be a practice of meditation and healing, and a way to access the subconscious.

Draw and color your own version of a mandala with patterns, symbols, and colors that are meaningful or pleasing to you.

Adjective Charades

One sign of a good actor is the ability to almost disappear into the role being played. Audiences may cease referring to that actor by his or her name and begin to think of the person as that character. For this exercise, you and a group of friends will attempt to disappear into a role—but to make it easier, you'll have just a single quality to represent.

To start, write a character trait onto a slip of paper; when you have enough for everyone to do at least two, place them into a hat. (A handful of traits are provided below to help get you started.) Shuffle the slips of paper and have everyone pull one paper out of the hat. Next, interact with one another, focusing on revealing your new character trait without actually saying what it is. After 5 minutes, try to guess each person's role.

SAMPLE ATTRIBUTES:

- hunchbacked
- barrel-chested
- frail
- hard of hearing
- flamboyant
- confident

- conceited
- clumsy
- athletic
- domineering
- humble
- gluttonous

Art History

"Cave paintings" is the term we have assigned the art created by our prehistoric ancestors (some of these paintings are more than 30,000 years old). Though we cannot know why these paintings were made, one of the many theories about the meaning of cave art is that it was a way for a particular tribe to document its history.

Try to convey the story of your life through your own version of "cave art," by using these pages to make a series of simple but evocative illustrations of the major events of your experience.

Symbol-ism

It's been said that "a picture is worth a thousand words." But for this exercise, one picture really is made up of words. Or letters. Or symbols.

Like the pointilists, who made images using only dots, you will draw a picture in the space below using only letters, numbers, and punctuation marks. Feel free to overlap the symbols, but each one must be complete. By the way, the letters don't have to be limited to block print. Consider script.

All At Sea

Imagine that the main floor of your house or apartment has been transformed into a raging sea.

Assuming that the furniture is not disrupted by the change of environment, map out the easiest ways to navigate through your newly wavy home without touching the "water." Feel free to use windowsills, built-in bookcases, and other items that can hold your body weight.

Deejay Daze

You just got word that your friends will be coming over for a party in one hour! Quickly assemble a playlist of twenty songs to serve as great background music.

1.
2.
3.
4.
5.
6.
7.
8.
9.
10.
11.
12.
13.
14.
15.
16.
17.
18.
19.
20.

Oops! you might need to get your ears checked because, in fact, you failed to hear one crucial word. Your *parents'* friends will be coming over for a party, not your friends! What does your playlist look like now? Would you use any of the same songs? Why?

1.
2.
3.
4.
5.
6.
7.
8.
9.
10.
11.
12.
13.
14.
15.
16.
17.
18.
19.
20.

Haiku You

A haiku is a poem of Japanese origin that is seventeen syllables long and is made up of three lines: the first line has five syllables, the second line has seven syllables, and the third line has five syllables. A haiku often takes the natural world as its subject.

Try writing a haiku for every season: spring, summer, fall, and winter.

> *Creativity represents a miraculous coming together of the uninhibited energy of the child with its apparent opposite and enemy, the sense of order imposed on the disciplined adult intelligence.*
>
> **NORMAN PODHORETZ**

Impromptu Chef

A staple of television cooking contests is the strange or limited ingredients list, which forces the contestants to come up with creative dishes. How would you fare? In our contest, you'll need to grab any not-food-related magazine, and write down the first 5 food items you see. Now develop an appealing recipe using just those ingredients.

Cell Madness

It's time for a new cell phone, but the phone company won't give you a new one unless you promise to repurpose the old one so it won't become landfill. Without relying on any of your phone's functions, write down and/or sketch 3 alternative uses for this item.

1.

2.

3.